SCENES OF THE PLATEAU LANDS AND HOW THEY CAME TO BE

by

WM. LEE STOKES
Professor of Geology
University of Utah

Sketches by the Author

Pedestal Rock

Cover is part of a drawing by W. H. Holmes, made for E. C. Dutton's classic report on the Tertiary history of the Grand Canyon, issued by the United States Geological Survey in 1882.

Copyright © 1969

Available from
Starstone Publishing Company
333 J Street
Salt Lake City, Utah 84103

19th Printing, 1997

Lithographed in the United States of America
PUBLISHERS PRESS
Salt Lake City, Utah

TABLE OF CONTENTS

ROCKS MAKE THE SCENE

We live on a rocky planet called Earth. Beneath the cover of vegetation and soil and even under lakes and oceans, all is stone. From the greatest continents down to the sand grains of the beach the essential constituents are various kinds of rocks. Man has had to deal with his rock-bound world in various ways. From small pieces of stone he learned at an early date to carve and chip weapons, tools, and ornaments. Soon he was piling larger pieces of stone into temples, towers, pyramids and dwellings. Later he learned to melt and dissolve other rocks to free the valuable metals contained therein. He burns a rock called coal. Even our most modern constructions of concrete, brick and mortar represent stone that has been crushed and recombined to fill the varied needs of civilization.

But all the stone-breaking, stone-moving and stone-gathering works of man are puny and have little effect upon the general landscape. Roads, cities, fields and farms must conform to shapes which the landscape provides. Hills, mountains, islands and continents are facts of existence to be accepted and adjusted to as best we can. Primitive people know the details of their surroundings as matters of survival but have no understanding of how earth features came into being or why they have the forms they now possess. Modern man has mapped most of the earth in detail and in addition knows something of how landscapes are shaped. The interpretation of scenery is a fascinating part of the study of the earth and is what this booklet is about.

This is not a discussion of rocks or minerals as such. It does not tell about the captive, classified specimens which have been gathered and stuffed into museums, or those carved and polished for human use, or those shaped and imprisoned in buildings, streets, and walls. Rather, we hope to tell something of the wild, crude, undomesticated, unused, and generally uncoveted rocks that make up the landscape of the plateau country.

Scenery is like art, the more we study it the more we enjoy it. The comparison goes even deeper, however, for just as there are different forms of art, so are there different types of natural landscapes. Fortunately we do not need to be highly trained students of the earth in order to make a useful classification of the natural features we live with or travel over. With a little study we can learn why landscapes, like works of art, can be grouped according to type. In these times when nearly everyone travels far and wide a little knowledge of "scientific seeing" will add greatly to a person's enjoyment and profit.

Nature, like a talented artist, works with a number of tools, uses various techniques, and many different materials to accomplish her effects. Water, wind, and ice become tools to carve the face of the earth. Nature may remove material by erosion or add to it by deposition, carving here, sculpturing there. The raw materials are varied: some hard, some soft, some uniform, some banded and varied in color and composition.

Water meets rock in
the desert thunderstorm

The process of creating a landscape is never finished. It is a continuing process—started ages ago, still going on, destined to proceed, never to be completed. To our time-bound minds a landscape may seem finished, perhaps even a masterpiece and we may enjoy it as we enjoy a single still scene from a motion picture; nevertheless we know that other scenes went before and will probably be succeeded by others in the future. This is the fascination of the study of landscape—to visualize what happened to create the scenes that now exist and to try to predict what might alter them in the future.

In the pages that follow we will take a close look at one chief type of scenery—one in which the chief tool has been running water, the chief technique has been erosion, and the chief material, beds of bare sandy rock. Our area is huge and a bit hard to define. It centers at the well known Four Corners where Utah, Colorado, Arizona and New Mexico meet. The traveler will already have heard of or seen parts of it—it contains the Grand Canyon, The Arches, Monument Valley, the Natural Bridges, Lake Powell, and a thousand other scenic spots. It corresponds closely with what geographers call the Colorado Plateau but goes beyond—it shares a part of the Great American Desert, the Southwest and even the Rocky Mountains broadly speaking. For want of a precise name, we will call it the Plateau Country, for here flat lying layers of rock give endless horizontal and vertical lines, outlining cliffs, mesas, buttes, and monuments in profusion.

The Plateau Country is not mountain, plain, or prairie. Vegetation, usually a dominant part of scenery is here spare and

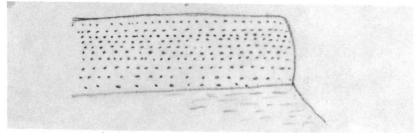

Dry climate, sparse vegetation
thin soil, sharp profiles

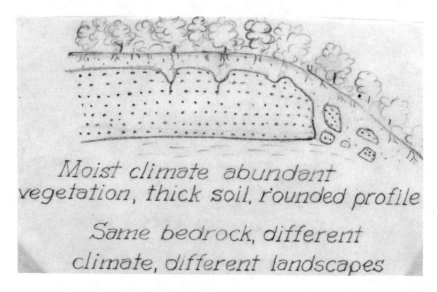

Moist climate abundant
vegetation, thick soil, rounded profile

Same bedrock, different
climate, different landscapes

scattered. Even soil, which softens and covers most landscapes is thin or absent. Water is scarce, and there are few rivers or natural lakes to attract the eye. Glacial ice has not touched this land. Here is truly a kingdom of rocks, an arena where the elemental forces of time and weather meet the raw stuff of the earth with nothing to soften or hide the scars of battle.

ROCKS
Hard and Soft

The old saying "hard as a rock" reminds us that most rocks are tough, durable and not easy to break. This idea comes from everyday experience with building stones, monuments, and pebbles of streams and beaches. All of these are unusually hard for rocks, it is their hardness which brings them to our attention.

Some rocks are not hard at all—geologists do not hesitate to call such rocks as chalk, shale or mudstone soft. These rocks crumble easily, and can be cut, broken, or crushed with little effort. They disintegrate easily into soil and hence we do not usually think of them as rocks. We make little or no use of them in building or construction.

Nature quickly and unerringly distinguishes between hard and soft rock by the processes of weathering and erosion. By noting the effects of erosion, we can tell which rocks are hard and which are soft even from a distance. The secret is simple: hard rocks withstand erosion better than soft ones and will be more prominent in any scene where hard and soft occur together. This means that hard rocks will eventually stand higher or protrude farther while soft rocks will stand lower or recede. This is the Principle of Differential Erosion.

Go into almost any old graveyard and look at the stones. On some the inscriptions and carvings are almost obliterated while others, just as old, are fresh and sharp. This is differential erosion in action. The forces of rain, frost, and sunshine have been equally strong everywhere—only the reactions of the stones has differed.

A fading inscription ~ weathering in action

This does not mean that all hard rocks stand high while all soft rocks are low. The comparison is good only where hard and soft are near enough together, like gravestones in a churchyard, to be subject to the same forces of destruction. Thus rocks that form cliffs are harder than those that form the slopes below them; peaks are generally harder than their foothills; natural monuments are harder than the bases on which they stand; ridges are harder than valleys; and on a cliff or stream bank the protruding layers are harder than those which form grooves.

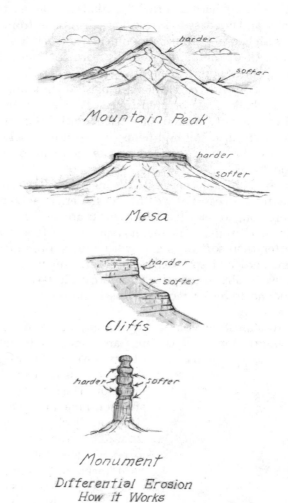

Mountain Peak

Mesa

Cliffs

Monument

Differential Erosion
How it Works

On an even smaller scale we see that there are differences in the hardness of pebbles. With the aid of a hammer we can soon arrange the rocks of a stream bed in their order of hardness. We will see that hard pebbles usually come from hard formations. A little more observation will tell us that the hard pebbles will last longer on a beach than the soft ones and that they will likewise travel farther in a stream. A patch of gravel that is made up of hard rocks is in itself very durable; gravel, even though it is not in solid beds, is strong enough to be a cap for hills and ridges.

Pebbles are the harder remnants of vanished rock formations

Small wonder that many of our precious and semi-precious stones as well as gold and platinum are gathered from stream beds or beaches where nature has sorted them by a process of natural selection.

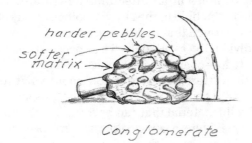

harder pebbles

softer matrix

Conglomerate

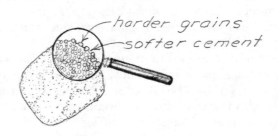

harder grains

softer cement

Sandstone

Differential Erosion

ROCKS
Large and Small

How large can a rock be? We think of some famous examples such as the Rock of Gibralter, St. Pauls Rocks, Stone Mountain, Georgia, or Sugarloaf Mountain near Rio De Janeiro. It is plain that the people who named these landmarks pictured a rock as being a large, prominent and solid piece of the landscape. In all these, however, the object called a rock is a mere surface bump attached to a much larger mass of material under the surface which is also rock. We hesitate to call a mountain a rock unless it has about the same appearance and composition from top to bottom.

Geologists and engineers know that there is nothing but rock under the surface of the earth, and that this rock is well packed and solid for hundreds of miles in all directions downward. The earth itself has been called a "pebble in the sky." Geologists may also refer to any kind of earth material that occurs in pieces large enough to see and deal with individually as a rock. The specialist may be very technical and refer to loose sand or even ice as rock.

Considering the differences of opinion about what rocks and rock material is, it is probably better to restrict ourselves to those separate pieces of solid material that can be seen to make up definite parts of the landscape. Here again geologists have been measuring and classifying—any piece more than 10 inches across is a boulder; cobbles come next 2½ to 10 inches across; and pebbles are smaller, from about ½ inch to 2½ inches across. Below this come various sizes of granules, sand and silt that do not individually stand out in the landscape. Again we should emphasize the idea that most of the rocks we are concerned with have broken off from larger masses such as cliffs, hills or mountains.

So to return to our original question of how large a rock can be, the average person means how large can single, unattached, unbroken pieces of rock be? It is doubtful that we can answer the question even with this definition for no one has made a career of measuring large unattached boulders. Suffice it to say that masses weighing thousands of tons may be found at the base of many high cliffs, along seacoasts, around volcanoes, or embedded in ice. These large pieces do not concern us much except as curiosities—we are more interested in the smaller pieces that make up ordinary stream beds or beaches or that lie on surfaces that once were stream beds or

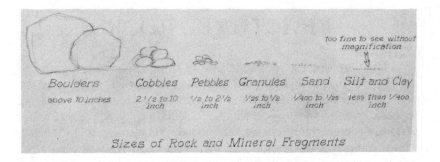

Boulders	Cobbles	Pebbles	Granules	Sand	Silt and Clay
above 10 inches	2 1/2 to 10 inch	1/2 to 2 1/2 inch	1/25 to 1/2 inch	1/400 to 1/25 inch	less than 1/400 inch

Sizes of Rock and Mineral Fragments

beaches.

The smaller pieces of rock which finally accumulate as gravel in stream beds or on beaches have literally stood the test of time to preserve their identity. They have survived the effects of weathering and erosion while weaker, softer pieces have been broken to dust. It is in a stream bed that rock fragments get their most severe beating. Here they are rolled and tumbled, battered and beaten until they are rounded and smooth. Any resting place is likely to be temporary, a pebble we see today may not have been there yesterday and may be miles on its way during the next flood, getting smaller and smaller as it goes. Weak rocks disappear first and after a few tens of miles only the very hardest remain—those made of quartz, quartzite, chert, gneiss, and flint; all extremely hard varieties. These will be rounded and smoothed, perhaps even polished, from their long journey in contact with each other and with churning sand. There is evidence that certain pebbles have travelled 500 miles by stream and still they are large enough to call gravel.

So gravel is composed of durable rocks winnowed and refined by nature for their toughness and hardness. In beds of gravel we search for precious and semi-precious stones, and here we get material for roads, for making concrete, and for lining driveways. A good gravel bed may be as valuable as a gold mine. We mention gravel especially here for we see a lot of it in plateau land, and it has a lot to do with some of the scenery there.

FRACTURED ROCKS

Most of the rocks we see are in broken pieces lying on the surface of the earth. It may be surprising to know that much of the breaking was done underground long before the rocks were revealed to view. Even in the deepest mines (11,000 feet) or oil wells (25,000 feet) the rocks are broken and fractured. Of course, under the earth where the pressure is tremendous the blocks are not yet separated, but the cracks along which they will eventually break are already there. Geologists refer to these unseparated cracks as joints and the blocks of rock which they outline are therefore joint blocks.

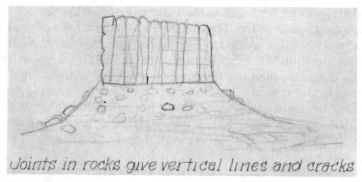

Joints in rocks give vertical lines and cracks

The origin of joints is really not well understood, but we know that rocks are brittle and that great stresses and strains exist in the crust of the earth that are sufficient to break even the strongest materials. It seems possible that it is these inner forces which cause the rocks to weaken and crack. Joints are mostly vertical and their surfaces are very smooth and even. A single joint may be only a few feet long or it may cut through the rocks for miles along a straight course. Joints come in groups of dozens or even hundreds and may be a few inches to many feet apart. When two sets or groups of joints cross one another the rocks are cut into nicely spaced blocks, most of which are diamond shaped. Because of joints the job of quarrying stones becomes easier since huge blocks may already be loose on several sides and do not need to be cut or split to break them out of their beds. On the other hand, too many joints are undesireable—many a fine piece of marble or granite cannot be used because it is cut by a joint which has weakened it.

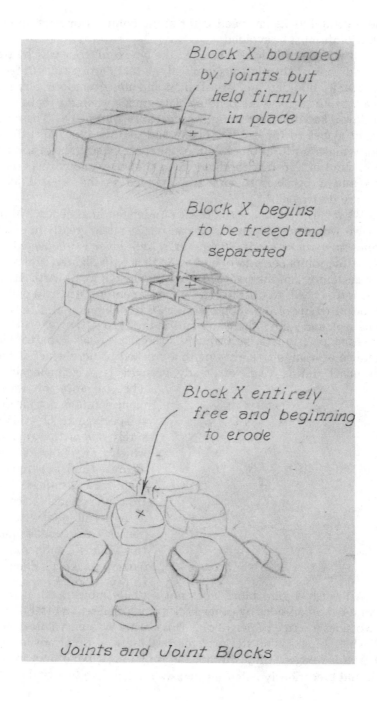

Joints and Joint Blocks

Where great blocks are needed for stone columns or large monuments joints must be avoided.

Now if you will look closely at the blocks of stone which litter the landscape of the plateaus you will see that certain sides or faces of the larger boulders are very straight and almost smooth. Some of these smooth surfaces are bedding planes made when the rocks were laid down, but the other smooth surfaces are joint planes. These run at right angles to the bedding planes and the two types of surfaces tend to make uniform blocks out of the rock. Of course as a boulder lies in the sun and rain for many years the edges and corners flake away and it becomes smooth and rounded as the original joint faces are destroyed.

What have joints got to do with understanding scenery? More than we would suspect at first because joints help greatly in determining how rocks erode. Whenever a rock layer is uncovered by erosion the joints begin to open up. At first only slightly, a relaxing after the removal of the great pressures that held it in the earth. Later other forces begin to operate—air and water enter the narrow cracks and begin to dissolve or combine with the rock material. Roots of plants seek and follow the water and as they grow, they exert ever-increasing pressure to split and pry the joint blocks apart. The spectacle of a large tree growing in a cracked boulder which it has split apart during years of steady pressure is a common sight.

Tree splits rock

The entrance of water along joints is not always so spectacular, but this is surely one of the ways in which large blocks are separated and prepared for their final disintegration. In colder climates ice is a powerful tool. As it freezes, water expands, and this force, if confined in a narrow crack, is sufficient to pry the rocks apart.

Although a joint block does not actually move much if it is surrounded on all sides by other rocks, it is a different matter if one or two sides are free of neighbors. This is what we see on almost any cliff where blocks in all stages of removal are seen. Some are deeply and firmly wedged, they will not fall for a long time; others are so loose and precariously balanced that we are tempted to give them a final nudge to send them crashing down the slope below. The final breaking away of a large block of rock from a cliff is accomplished when gravity can take effect. To bring about an unstable condition nature employs a subtle technique called sapping or undermining. As one side of a block is laid bare on a hillside there is an opportunity for weather and water to attack not only the freshly exposed side but also the softer material just beneath it. Rain dripping down the side may soak and wet the soft rock below causing it to flake or fall away. Soon a groove or depression is formed—it deepens and widens; the support for the overlying block becomes smaller and smaller. Finally, perhaps through the mere freezing of water in a joint plane on a cold night, or the push of new roots, or expansion by the heat of a morning sun, the rock topples and falls to the slopes below, shattering itself and others in the process.

Thus the blocks we see on a hillside were outlined by planes of weakness long before they reached the light of day. These planes became available to innumerable tiny wedges of ice, roots, and chemical reactions until perhaps gaping cracks were formed. With the removal of support on one or two sides the block was undermined by water and weather until one day it fell from its place in the cliff.

By the removal of a single block the total area of the hard layer is decreased. If the block falls from a hillside, the hill becomes a little bit smaller; if it falls from the side of a canyon, the canyon becomes a little bit wider. Difficult to believe though it may be, the slow removal, bit by bit, of joint blocks from cliff faces has apparently caused not only canyons but also valleys to widen tens of miles. Thus the cliffs of central Utah and those of the Mesa Verde in Colorado were once part of a continuous blanket of sandstone. Cut through by the Colorado and its tributaries, the cliffs began to form and crumble, drawing away from each other yard by yard until they are now literally beyond sight of each other.

Once a large block has been shattered by falling from its

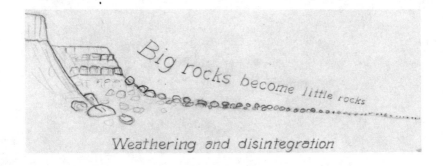

Big rocks become little rocks

Weathering and disintegration

original niche the pieces are subject to weathering and erosion from all sides and soon crumble to sand or dust. Look at any hillside in the Southwest. You will see large recently fallen blocks, older but smaller blocks down farther on the hillsides with smaller and smaller ones outward until none remains. Only through removal by talus creep and slow disintegration of old blocks and the breaking up of softer material can space be made for new material from the cliffs above.

THE COLORS OF ROCKS

Most rocks are drab and colorless. Marble, we carve into statues and monuments. Banded or patterned rocks we like to use in fireplaces, table tops, walls, and floors. All these come in rather small deposits and do not add much color to the general landscape. It is the color of the thick formations that make up canyon walls or mesas that is of interest here. The rocks of the plateau-country are among the most colorful on earth; in fact, the term "red-rock country" has been applied to parts of it. Here the rocks appear in their natural unobscured beauty with little competition rom vegetation. The scattered trees do not obscure the rocks, their green color accentuates and is accentuated by the red of the surrounding bedrock.

Whence comes the color of rocks? Most rocks are colored by iron compounds. Iron is the great pigment-maker. According to its chemical state and combinations it may be black, brown, red, yellow, gray, or green. And, like cake coloring, a little bit goes a long way. A mere trace is sufficient to give strong color to a formation. In a sandstone, the color is usually not in the sand grains themselves but in the cement between the grains.

Other colorful or color-making elements are carbon, which gives black; manganese, which gives black, brown, red, and purple; and copper, which gives chiefly green. But iron is far and away the most effective and abundant.

Most rocks are the same color inside and out, but there are a number of ways that desert surfaces can take on a paint-like cover of colored material that has no resemblance to the true or inside color.

The most common of desert coatings is "desert varnish" and it is well named for it is lustrous, shiny, and smooth, and forms only a thin surface coat. The colors produced range from light brown to black depending on how much has accumulated. Desert varnish occurs on all deserts and has attracted the attention of many explorers and scientists who have given different explanations for its origin.

Desert varnish can form on surfaces of all sizes from mere pebbles to great canyon walls hundreds of square yards in extent. It seems to form best on the harder types of rock with plenty of silica and those that are hard and dense; however, almost any rock can be

Cliff with streaks of desert varnish

coated. Varnish is thicker and darker on the upper surfaces of pebbles and on rock walls facing the sun. High temperatures from exposure to the hot desert sun seem to be helpful for a good healthy "tan" of desert varnish.

Beyond these observations of the facts there is some difference of opinion as to what else is involved. When desert varnish is chemically analyzed, it is found to be rich in manganese and iron that could come only from within the rock itself or at most from the soil on which the rocks lie. Some think that the mineral matter gets onto the rocks through the action of water that splashes or falls on it during rains or drips downward over the edge of cliffs. As the water evaporates the mineral matter is left a little at a time until a smooth coat is formed. Some investigators believe that bacteria living on the hot rock surfaces have the power to concentrate the necessary minerals in forms that cannot be washed away or dissolved.

Desert varnish is visible in almost any view of high smooth canyon walls of sandstone or lava in the plateaus. Here it appears in broad streaks of black or brown, looking much like dark paint spilled over the canyon walls. As one could observe after a storm, these dark strips are the areas that are wetted by downward moving films of water. This seems to prove that water is necessary to the process of formation. The darker streaks are obviously older than the lighter ones, and where the process has gone on for a very long time, the surface becomes smooth, almost black, and reflects the sun's rays like a mirror.

Varnished surfaces seem to have been a challenge to prehistoric artists who pecked or painted their mysterious "writings" on many such areas. By pecking through the outer dark coating to expose the lighter rock beneath, the artist could achieve a pleasing and lasting cameo-like image. Here we get a clue to how long it takes varnish to form. For some ancient writings have been "revarnished" after having been made. Later a second set of overlapping pictures may have been pecked. This seems to indicate that at least two thousand years are needed for the darker desert coatings to form.

Indian pictograph pecked on a desert varnish surface

An observant person will also see desert varnish over patches of pebbles. When these are seen as they reflect the rays of the sun in the early and later parts of the day, the effect is almost dazzling. Travelers in the Old World deserts apply descriptive terms such as "Valley of Gems" to these places.

Another type of superficial "paint" seen in certain areas is easier to explain than desert varnish. It appears where strongly colored material from one formation washes downward to cover a lower formation. The great Redwall Limestone, thickest, most prominent cliff-maker in the Grand Canyon, receives its name not because it is really a red rock but because it is colored red by fine red silt dripping down from the really red Supai Formation above.

Lichens growing on rock

Still another type of superficial material may color desert

rocks. This material is or has been alive and is made of lichen, a lowly form of vegetation. Lichens usually occur in spots and patches of different colors and may be gray, green, yellow or brilliant orange. Old dead patches may be black or white. Since these plants need at least a little water they may be most common on the shady side of cliffs or at the higher elevations. They grow with extreme slowness, a patch six inches across may be a hundred years or more old. Rub them and they break apart and flake away, but they leave curious shadowy scars where they were once attached.

CLIFFS

Steep, vertical or overhanging outcroppings of rock are called cliffs; they may also be called scarps or escarpments. Most cliffs extend for miles, keeping the same general height above their surroundings. Cliffs may stand alone or they may rise in steps above one another. They may be found near the bottoms of great canyons or on the highest mountains and so are common features of all rugged eroded lands. Vegetation and soil tend to soften and obscure rocky outcrops so that cliffs are not commonly seen in humid regions.

Although we can accept cliffs as a matter of course there are certain geological reasons why they exist. They are obviously harder than the materials on which they rest and that is the first reason for their prominence. They are steep for several reasons. In the first place, they are almost always cut by joints which are vertical or nearly vertical cracks; when a piece of cliff-face topples, the break usually follows one of these planes of weakness that does not slant strongly inward or outward. Another reason cliffs are mostly steep is that they are undermined from below so that just enough ma-

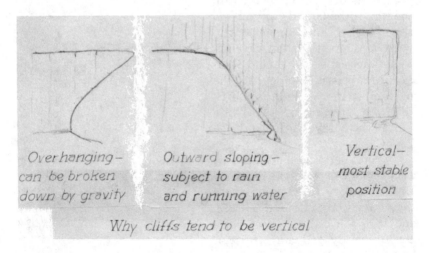

Overhanging —
can be broken
down by gravity

Outward sloping —
subject to rain
and running water

Vertical—
most stable
position

Why cliffs tend to be vertical

terial falls away to satisfy the pull of gravity. If part of a cliff leans out too far, it will probably fall sooner or later as it is weakened by weathering; if it does not protrude, of course, gravity cannot affect it until the underlying support is weakened. A vertical rock, like a man standing erect, is able to withstand gravity best. The undermining of cliffs takes place because the material underneath the hard cliff-forming layer is softer and can be removed by erosion with relative ease. Rain water trickling downward or even dew or moisture in the air can disintegrate soft shale or sandstone so that it loses all strength and flakes easily away. As the supporting material disappears, the rock above, no matter how hard or strong it may be, will also fall; a natural illustration of the parable of the statue with feet of clay.

The cliffs of the plateau land are high as well as long and are distinctively colored. In fact, it is their colors which gave them their popular names. Commencing with the rim of the Grand Canyon and rising higher and higher northward is a great system of cliffs sometimes called the Grand Staircase of Western Geology. At the bottom is the Vermillion Cliffs, followed upward by the White Cliffs, the Gray Cliffs, and the Pink Cliffs.

The Vermillion Cliffs run almost parallel with the Arizona-Utah boundary to the point where they intersect the Colorado River, and turn southward. These cliffs are brilliantly red and are well named. The lower part of the cliffs is shale, the upper part conglomerate and sandstone. Here are

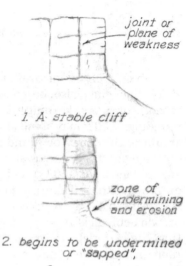

joint or plane of weakness

1. A stable cliff

zone of undermining and erosion

2. begins to be undermined or "sapped",

3. becomes unstable

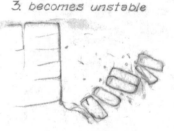

4. and falls

How cliffs retreat, a little at a time

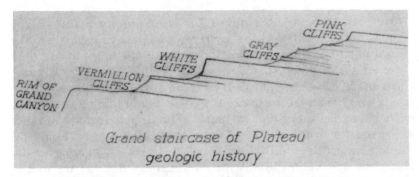

Grand staircase of Plateau
geologic history

found fossils of the Triassic Period of earth history. Included are some of the earliest dinosaurs, heavy bodied amphibians, fish, and marine shells. The conglomerate has many fossil trees and even extensive petrified forests. Above the Vermillion Cliffs are the White Cliffs. These make up probably the most famous escarpment in the West because of their height and the many picturesque forms into which they are carved. The White Cliffs are made almost entirely of one great sandstone layer, named the Navajo Formation because it is best known in the land of the Navajos. Since it is uniform from top to bottom it usually makes one great cliff. The traveler will see it best in Zion Park, but Glen Canyon (occupied by Lake Powell) and the Rainbow Bridge are also carved from it. This formation is a great "fossilized" desert made of solidified sand dunes piled one above another. Life on this ancient desert was scarce so there are few fossils—here and there a few animal tracks and poorly preserved dinosaur skeletons; enough to tell us we are in the Jurassic Period. The White Cliffs are almost impassable and run in unbroken majesty for miles along the canyons of the Colorado Plateau. Two famous crossings of the Colorado, Hole-in-the-Rock, and Crossing of the Fathers, are through the Navajo Formation.

Above the White Cliffs are the Gray Cliffs, somewhat obscure and retiring as they are made of soft shale that does not stand out as boldly as the harder rocks above and below. Rocks of the Gray Cliffs are mostly ocean-deposited and are well supplied with shells of sea life and teeth of sharks which lived in the Cretaceous Period. Beds of coal, created from swamp and marsh vegetation, mark this part of the area.

Capping the high plateaus of southern Utah are the Pink Cliffs, youngest of all. The parent rock is limy siltstone, a product of an ancient freshwater lake that once covered much of southeastern Utah. From this layer erosion has carved Bryce Canyon and Cedar Breaks, jewels of color and intricate form.

Starting from the bottom of the Grand Canyon and ascending upward cliff by cliff or layer by layer, one passes through a rocky record of most of the great periods of geologic time. In fact only three of the thirteen standard periods are lacking in this display. Cliffs made of rocks equivalent to those in the Grand Staircase are found everywhere in the plateau country. Many other great lines of cliffs have received distinctive names. The Grand Hogback in Colorado runs for over 200 miles; Comb Ridge, Waterpocket Fold, and the San Rafael Reef in Utah are on all the maps. In Arizona are the Hurricane and Echo Cliffs. With a little study one can see that in most of these the same formations, such as Navajo Sandstone, appear time and again.

Not to be overlooked is a particularly prominent and famous escarpment that runs across east-central Utah into Colorado. This is the Book Cliffs. Early explorers saw in these rock layers some resemblance to a well stocked bookshelf—the backs of the books being outlined by evenly spaced vertical cracks—hence the name Book Cliffs. Rising above these are the Roan Cliffs, another color name, and finally the Badland Cliffs over the upper edge of which one can look into the bowl-shaped Uinta Basin. The Badland Cliffs are about equivalent in age to the Pink Cliffs farther south.

A large part of the human history of the plateau can be written in terms of its cliffs. The location of almost all the towns, roads, railroads, dams, and cultivated areas have had to be determined with due regard to these great natural barriers.

MESAS AND BUTTES

The term "mesa country" is applied to many areas of the southwest. "Mesa" is Spanish and means table, a mesa is a hill with a relatively smooth, flat, table-like top. In the mesas we have a perfect example of the principle that hard rocks stand higher and protect soft rocks and also that hard rocks are usually removed by undermining their edges. The cap or top of a mesa may be one of several hard types of rock such as sandstone or lava. Strangely enough, it may also be nothing more than gravel, which we might not ordinarily consider to be a "hard rock."

Since there are great numbers of alternating sandstone and shale beds in the Southwest, conditions are favorable for mesas to form with caps of standstone and bases of shale. These common types may cover hundreds of square miles, like that most famous of all western mesas, the Mesa Verde in southwestern Colorado, or they may be only a few square acres in extent. They are flat on top because of the fact that the capping layers are still in the level position in which they were laid down and because erotion has removed the softer rocks that were once above the cap rock.

The "rim" or cliff which surrounds the level upper surface may be high or low depending on the thickness of the protecting bed. If the "rim" is high it may not be easy to cross or climb. Many mesas have no easy pathways to the top, and on some of them fortresses and even sizeable towns have been constructed which could be protected by defending the few passable trails.

The slopes around a mesa are almost everywhere covered with blocks broken from the rims. This debris proves that mesas, like other high-standing features, must get smaller and eventually disappear.

A large proportion of western mesas are capped by hard layers of sandstone or conglomerate. A hard layer is essential but there may also have been at one time an overlying soft layer that has disappeared and there must be an underlying soft layer that forms the slopes and most of the mesa itself. The arrangement of alternating hard and soft layers is common enough in the great piles of sedimentary rocks that exist—it requires only erosion to carve them into final form. A mesa does not start as a mesa, it begins to emerge when a succession of hard and soft layers is cut into by a river or

Erupted lava flows down valley

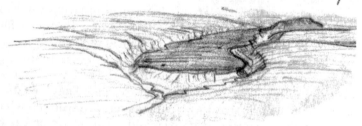

Streams cut channels along
sides of hardened lava

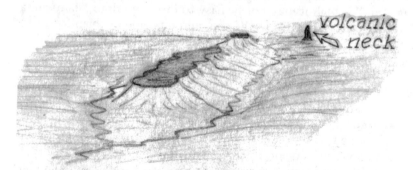

volcanic
neck

General erosion leaves the
hard lava of the former
stream as a capping for
a mesa

How a hill or ridge may form
where there was once a valley.

brought up by a fault. Then begins the etching out of the hard layer by the stripping away of surrounding material. Soon a bench or terrace is formed as the surface on top of the hard layer gets wider and wider. This cliff and surface is still attached to the canyon wall or mountain side, however, and has no separate identity. But smaller tributaries soon cut into the projecting shelf or terrace so that a number of points or headlands begin to protrude. These are free on two or three sides and it remains only for erosion to cut through the remaining side to create true mesas.

Lava-capped mesas, with their dark colored rims and slopes of shattered boulders are less common than the sandstone varieties. Mostly they have a more complex and interesting story for, believe it or not, in most cases the lava caps were once in valley bottoms and not on hilltops where we see them now.

The story of a lava-capped mesa begins with an outpouring of fiery molten lava. Lava, especially the kind which gives rise to dark-colored basalt, is very fluid and can run like water for miles before it finally hardens. So when such lava breaks forth from a volcano it seeks the nearest low ground and occupies any stream beds or valleys that may be nearby. Most amazing evidence of this is the solidified lava which clings like a frozen waterfall to the north walls of the Grand Canyon. A stream of lava from a relatively small volcano broke to the surface near the edge of the canyon. It tumbled in a fiery cascade over the edge and reached the river far below. Not only did it reach the river but it dammed it and followed the bottom of the canyon for at least 70 miles before it cooled. What a spectacle this must have created as fire and water contended in steam and smoke for possession of the canyon bottom!

But back to our story of how lava in a stream bed can become a mesa top. Of course lava can easily take over a stream bed by pushing the water aside and converting it to clouds of steam. It may even dam the stream to form lakes or ponds. Such lava-dammed lakes are indeed quite common; Navajo Lake in southwest Utah is a good example. But water usually has its way in the end because the life of a lava flow, although spectacular, is short, while a stream of water is much longer. The Colorado has practically cleared its course of the lava which once obstructed it. In a more open valley a stream will eventually reoccupy its valley along the margins of the cold beds of the former lava flow. Now again, we have a contrast of hard and soft rock. Lava is harder than sand or gravel or almost any sedimentary rock, and this is soon made evident by the way the stream begins to take over its former valley. The center of the valley or actual stream bed is, of course, occupied by the lava that cannot be easily eroded, but there are two parallel bands, one on either side of the lava flow, where the going is easier. Here water can find a course between the former bank or valley side and the lava, and here it begins to cut new courses, one on either side.

As the banks are lowered by the streams and its tributaries, the lava is left literally high and dry in the middle of the former valley. After much erosion the lava will be the high part of the region—in fact it may become a mesa. If we look at the base of such a mesa cap, we may see that it lies on a layer of gravel—the bed of the stream that it displaced the day it was fiery molten lava.

A Mesa...

becomes a butte...

becomes a spire...

and disappears.

The greatest lava-capped mesa in the west is appropriately called Grand Mesa. It is near Grand Junction, Colorado, which it overlooks from the east. Local residents call it the highest flat-topped mountain in the world. Where the lake-spotted lava now lies was once a broad open valley; now it overlooks two valleys, one on either side.

Finally, there are many mesas capped only by gravel. These usually lie along stream sides or where streams formerly ran in the past. Gravel is made of hard rocks and patches of gravel are about as durable as solid rock material itself. So by erosion it commonly happens that material is removed from around the edges of gravel banks or old stream beds leaving the patches more or less untouched. The process is similar to that of the lava-capped mesas. The areas which were low in the stream bed eventually become high by being preserved longer. Geologists call this action "topographic reversal."

One may justifiably ask about the difference between a mesa and a "butte". Buttes are the remnants of mesas and are so called when the object described is at least as high as it is wide. In other words mesas are wider than they are high, buttes are as high as they are wide. When a butte becomes very slender and there is practically no area in its top, it may be called a monument or spire.

CANYONS

When we look into the Grand Canyon we are naturally inclined to think it was cut by the Colorado River which winds, barely visible, in the depths below. But this is not entirely accurate; the Colorado River has actually cut only a small fraction of the Grand Canyon. The river itself has worn away only a narrow strip or groove scarcely wider than the stream bed itself, similar to the cut a saw blade makes in a plank of wood. The remainder of the canyon has been widened after the river had made the first furrow by the countless tributaries of all sizes that began to form on the sides, by the smaller gullies and rills that line all the slopes, by the falling, sliding, and crumbling of the cliff walls; in fact, by any and every action which loosens and moves material toward the river below.

Before men began to think logically about the history of the earth it was generally believed that canyons were original features dating back to the Creation, that they were left by the Flood as it receeded, or that they were created as great cracks or splits to be occupied by rivers later on. But careful thought and observation produced a more reasonable explanation: canyons (and other valleys) are cut by the rivers and tributaries that flow through them. For this very simple idea to be true we need only plenty of time, and there seems to be enough of that.

It is not uncommon to hear a tourist give expression to the thought that the Grand Canyon is a fault or giant crack, opened by a great upheaval. But most persons with a little reflection can be convinced that everyday erosion, given enough time, could do the job. The same goes for all the canyons, large or small, that furrow the plateau lands. We find here and there a canyon which follows a fault, but we know from looking in the very bottoms of most canyons that the rocks of practically all are solid and unbroken. In other words, if the river follows a fault the fault should be found in the bottom of the canyon.

We note that there are various kinds of canyons, some are shaped like a sharp-pointed V, some are mere straight-walled slits, narrow, winding and deep; others have step-like sides, with slopes and cliffs alternating upward towards the edge or "rim rock". There is a reason for these differences. Consider the stair-step variety and you will note that it is formed of alternating soft and hard layers.

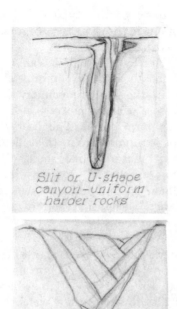

Slit or U-shape canyon—uniform harder rocks

V-shape canyon—uniform softer rock

Stair-step canyon—alternating hard and soft layers

Three canyon profiles

The hard layers form the risers or cliffs while the soft layers form the treads or more gently sloping parts. The cliffy parts are wearing back as cliffs do in arid regions and the slopes are following closely after as they are worn away by falling rain and running water.

The Grand Canyon is the world's best example of the stair-step type of canyon, but there are hundreds of others formed wherever the sides are made of alternating hard and soft layers. Another good place to view step-like river sides is from Dead Horse Point near Moab, Utah.

The narrow, slitlike canyons impress us. The walls are vertical or may even overhang. There are no steps in the walls, the depths are gloomy and echoing, stars are said to be seen in some spots at midday in the skies above. And woe to the traveler who is caught unaware in one of these canyons by a sudden flood. This type of canyon is formed in harder rocks that are of the same composition from top to bottom. It is really cut chiefly by the stream that runs in it. Here the swirling water filled with grains of sand and larger rocks of all sizes literally wears its way downward like a saw cutting into tough wood. Since there is no opportunity to undermine one part more than another the canyon remains narrow and of almost the same width as it wears downward. Even the Grand Canyon

Slit-like canyon in sandstone of uniform hardness

would be of this type if it had been cut in the same type of rocks from top to bottom.

Truly V-shaped canyons without the step-like profile are rare in the Plateau country for there are usually many hard layers to form cliffs. The best V-shaped canyons are in thick beds of soft material like shale. Of course, V-shaped canyons are common in humid areas where soil and vegetation soften and cover the rocks below.

Anyone who watches western movies knows about box canyons, those natural corrals or traps for outlaws. Somewhere along its course the side walls of a box canyon abruptly close and an impassable wall is formed. The stream bed continues upstream on a higher level, and any water running over the cliff creates a temporary waterfall.

Box canyons form when a major stream cuts down faster than its tributaries. Since they cannot keep up with the downcutting master stream the tributaries lag behind and enter it by falling from a higher level. But the tributary can cut backward away from the master stream so that the original fall or step moves away to form short, high-walled, box-like canyons.

BADLANDS

What is a badland and what makes it bad?

The best badlands are bad for a number of reasons and paradoxically the better they are the more utterly bad they are. A good or well-developed or very bad badland is practically waterless and without vegetation. It is usually hot and oppressive with bewildering monotonous scenery. But the worst of all, the badland is almost all slopes, and anyone who travels over it will be continually ascending or descending an endless succession of hillsides so steep that climbing rather than walking is required. Detours avail nothing for the streamways seldom seem to go where the traveler is headed. The gullies are too narrow and the ridges are too sharp for easy pathways. Wheeled vehicles are out of the question, and horses and mules are more of a problem than an aid.

Lost in the badlands ?

It is fortunate that badlands usually come in small patches. The largest area of badlands is in South Dakota and Nebraska. A part of this has been set aside as a national monument. There are thousands of other smaller badlands going by such colorful names as Hell's Half Acre, Devil's Kitchen, and so forth.

A number of things seem essential to make a really bad (or good) badland. First, it must lie between a high area and a low area. The difference of elevation should be measured in tens or hundreds of feet and the descent from the high to lower ground should take place in a short distance. Thus badlands commonly form on the sides of mountains, hills or mesas or between two almost level areas in the plains.

Badlands form in relatively soft, half-hardened rocks, not in soil, not in hard sandstone or limestone. In this softer type of material, as we mentioned in the section on canyons, the typical drainage channel has a V-shape. When we put a lot of V's together we get an intricate system of gullies and ridges.

Finally badlands should be bare of vegetation, soil, or weathered waste such as gravel. Soil and vegetation would soon soften the sharp barren outlines, choke the stream channels and check erosion.

Then, of course, the area wouldn't be bad at all. The effect of gravel is not so clear, but it too would cause the stream beds to widen and take on U shapes rather than V shapes. In fact, there would be a tendency for the country to become smooth rather than rugged. Perhaps it is because the above conditions are seldom met that badlands are not too common or extensive.

Two of the most famous badlands in the West are Bryce Canyon National Park and Cedar Breaks National Monument in southern Utah. These are not entirely badlands for they include part of a flat higher surface and some lower country as well. The chief attractions are mostly fanciful monuments that add to and accentuate the badland scenery. Bryce Canyon is an area with almost no soil, very little vegetation, and only a little loose gravel. It is not really a canyon, for it lies on the side and edge of a plateau so that most of its scenic features are in the branching headwaters of several streams. The slopes here are so steep that water from the snow and occasional rains runs off very rapidly, taking with it any loose material that is available. As a result, bare rock is everywhere present on the surface or a few inches underground. There is enough water for plants and soil, but conditions are such that they cannot get a good start.

Badland forms
BRYCE CANYON

The rocks in Bryce Canyon are best described as limy siltstones. Silt is made of hard fragments smaller than sandgrains, consequently siltstone is a very fine grained sedimentary rock. Between the silt grains and also in fairly pure beds is limestone or calcite which is formed chemically and not laid down as particles. Limy siltstone is a moderately hard rock, and because it is neither too hard nor too soft it may appear not only in vertical walls such as hard rocks form but also in slopes such as soft rocks form. Also since the limy layers are harder than the silty layers there is a reason for the alternation protruding ridges and indented grooves that are so common here. Multitudes of grooved vertical monuments in the form of walls, castles, cathedrals, temples, and fanciful figures resembling people or animals are the rule. The mixture of shapes and forms of all kinds

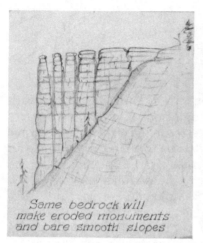

Same bedrock will make eroded monuments and bare smooth slopes

is what makes Bryce Canyon so fascinating.

Although the wind is said by some to be partly responsible for carving Bryce Canyon and similar areas, its role is greatly overrated. Wind is given credit for much more than it really deserves. Bryce Canyon for instance is in a sheltered spot on the side of a plateau where there is very little wind, and there are no sand dunes such as almost always occur in wind carved country.

ARROYOS, WASHES AND GULLIES

A river system is like a tree in that it has a main trunk with branches that get smaller and more numerous outward. In both trees and rivers we are usually more interested in the trunk and may come to consider the branches to be of little use or importance. Thus our attentions focus on the great trunk stream of the Colorado River and on the Grand Canyon through which it flows. Major tributaries such as the Dolores, San Juan, and Little Colorado are also fairly large permanent streams running in great canyons with their own characteristic scenery and geologic history, but the smaller-sized tributaries are known only locally. Even these smaller dry canyons were cut by water, however, and there is good evidence that they may have had permanent streams not many hundreds of years ago. As we follow upward along these dry tributaries we eventually reach even smaller branches that do not merit being called canyons at all. Depending where we are, these may be termed arroyos, washes, or simply gullies. The name arroyo seems to have come from Spain and is used in areas where Spanish influence has spread. "Wash" is more of an English word and has a connotation of wave action. The term "gully" seems to apply to something smaller and shallower than an arroyo, or wash, and brings to mind a minor or very small tributary on sloping ground. Also, when we think of gullies we imagine a lot of them close together, not one every few miles.

Generally the smaller tributaries are cut in soil or other soft material. Here erosion is rapid, and the streams pick up most of their load of mud and silt. The process of "gullying" or "arroyo cutting" is a part of the greater problem of soil erosion. Much attention has been paid to the destruction of soil since man and his sheep and cattle arrived in the Southwest. The problem of erosion of soil is indeed serious, but any observant person can see that erosion of rocks and soil is a process that has been going on for millions of years on an extensive scale and cannot be prevented or even long delayed by man.

A typical arroyo has a flat bottom—in fact many arroyos are so broad, flat and smooth that a car can travel along them for miles without trouble. Arroyos are distinctly not V-shaped, they are U-shaped. The bottom is commonly covered with gravel, and the sides are steep and are composed of soft alluvium, or

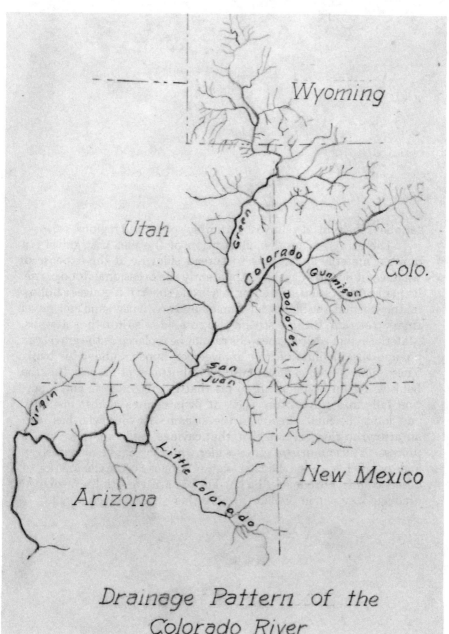

Drainage Pattern of the
Colorado River

The flat-bottomed arroyo in flood

"adobe", the typical yellowish, crumbly soil of arid regions.

The arroyo is another illustration of the idea that gravel is a durable material that tends to spread sidewise at the expense of whatever it lies on or against. Apparently the occasional flood carries its load of gravel and sand along in a broad sheet; if it gouges a hollow in the bottom, the hollow fills immediately with new sand and gravel from up stream. But the stream also cuts sidewise into the soft walls. Material removed from the walls cannot be replaced as the gravel can be, and so a definite nick or groove soon appears under the bank. These little side nicks may also have bottoms of gravel. But the bank will soon be undercut so far that it will collapse, and a portion falls into the stream where it disintegrates almost instantly and joins the mud already in the stream. Anyone who has seen an arroyo in flood knows that the cavings banks are part of the process. Thus an arroyo grows wider while the banks remain steep and parallel and the bottom flat. Arroyos are trade marks of desert country. Compare the flat-bottom arroyo with the V-shaped drainage-way cut in badlands where there is no gravel or sand.

MONUMENTS
Spires and Splinters

The names applied to the smaller erosional forms of the desert are almost endless. Although no general term like mesa or butte has come into general use, the term monument may be applied to those final remnants that are much higher than they are wide and which therefore bear some resemblance to living things or to the works of man. Of course, the higher and more slender they are the more they stand out—just as a skyscraper stands out among buildings. Color adds interest, and there may be endless variations of plain or ornamented surfaces and of horizontal and vertical bands, lines, crevices, cracks, grooves, and mouldings.

Architectural terms come to mind in describing many of these forms, for they have real or fanciful resemblance to man-made buildings. There are towers, castles, temples, spires, cathedrals, churches, monuments, and statues. We find many specific examples, recognized officially on maps as local landmarks: Temple Mountain, Cathedral Valley, Castle Valley, City of Rocks, Church Rock, Capitol Reef are well known. Some monuments resemble pieces of furniture or household objects: Cleopatra's Chair, Candlestick Tower, The Great White Throne, Tables of the Sun, Organ Rock, Jacob's Chair, Woodenshoe, Teapot Rock, the Flowerpot, Looking Glass Rock, Cleopatra's Needle, and the Cookie Jar, to name only a few.

THE TOTEM POLE
MONUMENT VALLEY

Strange as it seems in this desert land, a few forms are named for ships. Perhaps the best known landmark of the Four-Corners area is Shiprock, which rises abruptly from the New Mexico plains and can be seen for scores of miles in almost any direction. Near Moab, Utah is a marine tableau in stone, the Monitor and Merimec, two buttes that are good representations of their historic fighting counterparts. In Bryce Canyon one sees the Sinking Ship, a striking rock rising like a giant steamer about to take its final plunge.

Animals, too, are represented. Some have vague, unidentifiable forms like The Beast near Kayenta. The Parade of the Elephants is a major attraction in Arches National Monument, and the Elephants Feet, near Bluff, Utah are well named. Fishmouth Cave, Camelback Ridge, The Bears Ears, and Owl Rock are identified with little difficulty.

JACOB'S MONUMENT

STANDING ROCK
180 feet high

The human form, complete or in part, is duplicated in many monuments. The Mother of Castle Valley, in appropriate pioneer costume looks over southern Castle Valley; Bryce Canyon has its Queen Victoria; Family Butte in the San Rafael Swell resembles father, mother, and a number of children. Valley of Standing Men appears as a gathering place of a crowd of giant brooding figures. Los Gigantes, the Giants, rise in northeastern Arizona. Navajo Twins at Bluff, Utah are doll-like figures carved from sandstone. The Priest and Nuns near Moab, Utah require but little imagination to visualize. Picturesque though they may be, many anatomical names have had to be eliminated from maps (but not from local usage) in an effort to keep everything clean and fit for modern times.

Even articles of clothing are memorialized; Mitten Butte in Monument Valley is a pair of uplifted mittens, complete with thumbs; Mexican Hat, wide brimmed and well proportioned, is one of the best-named landmarks of southeastern Utah; Woodenshoe Butte needs no explanation.

Best known of all areas of erosion remnants is Monument Valley, shared by Utah and Arizona. Here the successive stages of formation of erosional forms from a thick sandstone layer are well shown. Around the Valley are wide bands of flat sandstone which we would describe as unbroken by erosion, like a large cake not yet cut into sections. From this unbroken rim many tongues or points of rock extend valleyward and are not yet separated from the main mass. They are attached on one side at least to the parent layer.

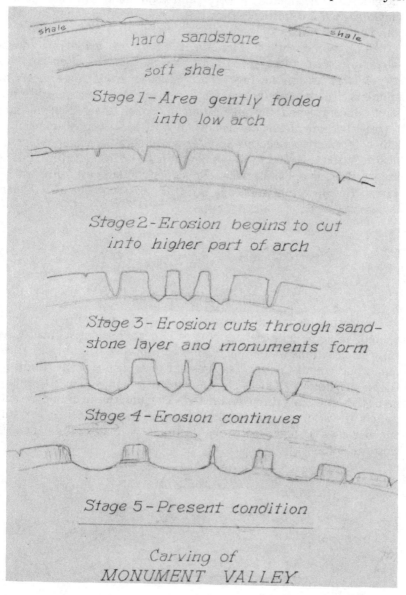

shale   hard sandstone   shale

soft shale

Stage 1 – Area gently folded
into low arch

Stage 2 – Erosion begins to cut
into higher part of arch

Stage 3 – Erosion cuts through sandstone layer and monuments form

Stage 4 – Erosion continues

Stage 5 – Present condition

Carving of
MONUMENT   VALLEY

Further out in the Valley are the eye-catching scenic monuments cut off and separated from the walls. Many are flat topped and boxlike, true mesas. Because of the way in which the great sandstone beds erode, the monuments keep the same uniform height while becoming narrower and more slender. Those which have reached a condition where they are higher than they are wide can be called buttes.

The monuments of Monument Valley are made of uniform sandstone, that is the same from top to bottom. As a consequence steps. They are in the process of falling apart in huge sheets or splinters. These monuments are not changeless—the parent sandstone once covered the area in an unbroken sheet. Benches and terraces became mesas, mesas became buttes, buttes became spires, spires toppled to become boulders, boulders became pebbles or disintegrated to sand. So it will continue to be in the future, but as long as there is raw material and a proper climate new forms will be carved to renew the landscape in future ages whether or not man is here to see it.

TRAIN ROCK

It is interesting to know how western landmarks have been named. In some areas where college educated scientists made the early explorations we find many names from classical subjects: thus, numerous Grand Canyon features get their names from Hindu or Greek mythology. The Mormons lent a religious flavor to many names in the area they colonized. The unlettered pioneers and miners drew upon the familiar facts of their existence for still another class of names. History itself can be read in the names of western landmarks.

SOME CANYONS IN PARTICULAR

The heart of the plateau country is called the Canyonlands, and it is well named. Here erosion is expressed in a wilderness of barren rock like nothing else on earth. All the streams are tributary to the

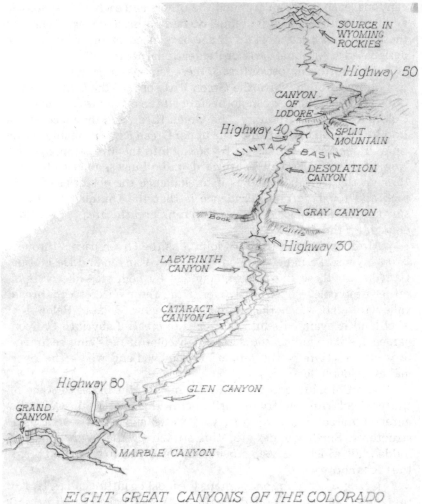

EIGHT GREAT CANYONS OF THE COLORADO
(And where to get across)

Colorado River; as it cuts downward they must follow. The work of keeping up with the great master stream has been tremendous. We wonder how the small or temporary streams could have excavated the canyons in which they run.

The Colorado River is unusual in many ways. Its headwaters are far from the canyon area where it is best known, and its mouth is equally far away in the different world of the Gulf of California. It is in its middle course that it has accomplished its greatest work.

The Green River and Colorado River pass through seven great canyons, each different from all the others and each with a geologic and human history that is unique. So fascinating and magnificent are these canyons that most of them have been or probably will be designated as National Parks or Recreational areas.

The northernmost or first of these famous gorges is the Canyon of Lodore through which the Green River crosses the Uintah Mountains. Only a geologist can appreciate all the events which gave the Colorado its chief tributary, the Green River, and the place of the Lodore Canyon in this story. The upper Green River probably at one time drained eastward across Wyoming into the Mississippi system. Now it turns suddenly southward and plunges almost directly through the Uintah Range as if to challenge the obstacles of hard rock and rough terrain. Evidence is that the Uintah Range and surrounding area once collapsed and sank and the area became low enough for the river to cross.

After leaving the Uintah Mountains the Green passes through two canyons of a more common type, Gray Canyon and Desolation Canyon. In these the river is bounded by high step-like cliffs of rather drab color. At Green River, Utah the river crosses a broad valley through which the railroad and highway pass. Below the level land it again cuts into the rocks to create Labyrinth Canyon named for its winding course through colorful flat-lying sedimentary strata. Here is the famous Bowknow Bend where the river makes a double loop.

The Colorado and Green Rivers meet in the midst of some of the most colorful country on earth. Below the junction the Colorado enters Cataract Canyon, with wild water and chaotic geological structures. Small wonder, for this stretch overlies a great bed of hidden salt which has been moving and dissolving to upset and break the rocks above.

Next is Glen Canyon, perhaps the most beautiful and restful of the gorges and now flooded by the waters of Lake Powell behind Glen Canyon Dam. Here the river and canyon follow great smooth

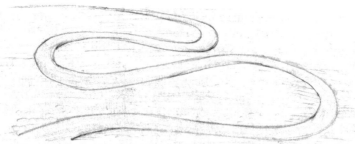

First stage — River meandering on low-lying plain

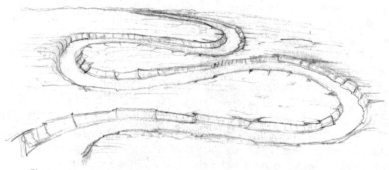

Second stage — Region is uplifted, river begins to cut downward without changing pattern

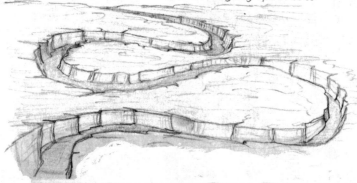

Third stage — River is completely enclosed in high canyon walls, but still follows the original curving course. This is the stage reached by many rivers in the Colorado Plateau.

ORIGIN OF INCISED MEANDERS
Curving rivers within deep canyons

meandering curves. This curving course presents another mystery the solution of which tells something more of the past history of the Colorado. Meanders are formed by rivers like the Mississippi flowing on broad open valleys. The Colorado at one time flowed on such a surface and has now buried itself in solid rock but has preserved its former pattern in detail. It has been estimated that the river has lowered itself about 2,000 feet into the earth destroying its former plain as it did so.

The greatest of the Colorado canyons is the Grand Canyon. It is 250 miles long, over a mile deep, and about ten miles wide at the narrowest part. Rough water and rapids abound, and a journey through it is counted as a major adventure. It is one of the world's greatest geological spectacles—about one third of the main periods of earth history and are recorded in its walls.

There are other notable canyons in the plateau cut by tributaries of the Colorado. The Black Canyon of the Gunnison, in a National Monument near Delta, Colorado, is deep and narrow and cut in hard, dark, and ancient rock like that in the bottom of the Grand Canyon. The San Juan River above its junction with the Colorado is also famous in geologic and historic lore. Its meandering course is even more winding than that of the Glen Canyon which it joins. The great Goosenecks of the San Juan where the river makes three tight loops within the space of one and one half miles is a fine example of incised meanders.

We have mentioned only the greater, better known canyons; hundreds of others exist, each with a character of its own.

NATURAL BRIDGES, ARCHES AND WINDOWS

Of all the natural wonders of the plateau-lands its perforated rock walls are the most unusual. The word "perforated" indicates that an opening of some type has been made through a mass of rock. These openings may be called bridges, arches, or windows depending on where they occur. Naturally, a bridge might be expected to cross a stream whether it be man made or of the so-called natural variety. Not too many openings meet this requirement but those which do are truly magnificent. An arch does not necessarily bridge a stream or channel; it is merely an opening through a wall of rock and may be of almost any shape or size. If an arch happens to open high on a wall, it might then be termed a window.

The number of arches, bridges and windows that decorate and enliven the plateau lands runs into the hundreds. Eighty-eight openings large enough to be classed as arches have been counted in the Arches National Monument alone. Natural Bridges National

ANGEL ARCH
Canyonlands National Park

Monument embraces three great natural bridges—Kachina, Sipapu, and Owachomo. Rainbow Natural Bridge, greatest of them all, stands in a class by itself and is honored by being in its own private national monument. Other famous stone arches include Grosvenor Arch a few miles east of Bryce Canyon; Cathedral Arch, White Mesa, Arizona; Metate Arch, near Escalante, Utah; and Hondo Arch southeast of Emery, Utah. Within Bryce Canyon there are numerous openings in the narrow sculptured walls; one of these is called the Wall of Windows. Less well known now but destined for future fame are the numerous arches and windows in Canyonlands Park. Here are literally dozens of fantastic forms including Angel Arch and Druid Arch, both of surpassing beauty.

The formation of natural arches must always begin with a narrow wall or plate of rock through which the opening is to appear. These thin walls of rock are mostly due to joints, of which we have already spoken. Joints, you will recall, are parallel smooth-walled cracks which cut steeply upward through the rock. They provide passageways for water and roots and tend to widen into gaping cracks as erosion progresses. *If* two joints grow and widen within a few feet or few yards of each other the thin wall of stone that is

CASTLE ARCH
Canyonlands National Park

necessary for an arch or window will be present. *If* the narrow wall somehow protrudes to view and is exposed to weathering, the situation is even more favorable. Now, once in a very great while if these conditions are met, the wall may be broken through in one spot before it wears away entirely and an opening will result. This opening may be widened or lengthened rather easily because erosion can now work on all the edges and gravity helps the process. It is no accident that Arches National Monument is one of the most jointed areas known, with literally thousands of parallel cracks which create slabs for cutting into fantastic shapes and openings. Here, as at other places, the upper part of the dominant sandstone is harder than the lower part; so other things being equal, it is easier to perforate the lower part and thus create arches in profusion.

Hard cap rock

DELICATE ARCH

So much for the usual arch or window. The formation of large natural bridges comes about in an entirely different way and joints have little to do with it. The four great natural bridges of southeastern Utah are large, massive structures. Kachina Bridge has a span of 203 feet and a height above the stream bed of 108 feet. Sipapu Bridge is more graceful and slender; 53 feet thick, 268 feet long, and 167 feet above the canyon floor. The "roadway" across it is 30 to 50 feet wide. Owachomo is 27 feet wide, 180 feet long and about 100 feet high. Rainbow Bridge, an arch of almost geometric perfection, is also a giant, rising 309 feet above the stream with a span of 278 feet. In this same area are the ruins of several bridges that have fallen, and others that are in process of formation. All these natural bridges occur on streams with winding curves known as meanders. These curves are cut down in the solid rock so that canyons and streams are both very crooked. Now it frequently happens that a stream will make a great curve and come back so as almost to meet itself—it has, in other words, traveled almost in a circle before it commences to swing in the opposite direction. Of course no river can flow in a circle, but if it *almost* meets itself it has created the thin wall of rock between the curves that is needed for the formation of a natural opening.

During floods the swirling water may strike against both sides of the narrow neck cutting it thinner and thinner. During low-water

KACHINA NATURAL BRIDGE
108 feet from stream bed to base of arch
203 foot span

SIPAPU NATURAL BRIDGE
268 foot span
167 feet from stream bed
to base of bridge
bridge 53 feet thick

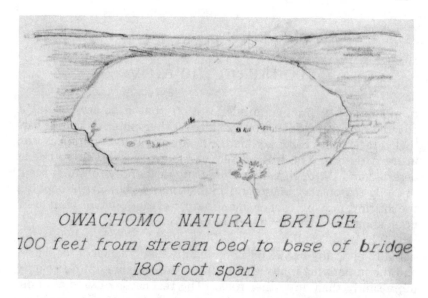

OWACHOMO NATURAL BRIDGE
100 feet from stream bed to base of bridge
180 foot span

stages there will be a natural percolation of water through the wall to weaken it still more. One day there comes a complete breakthrough and the stream leaves its old curving course for a shorter one under a bridge of its own creation.

In all the great natural bridges the story is plain to see. There is the older abandoned channel on the side and the river course branching from it to pass under the bridge.

DOUBLE ARCH
Arches National Monument

A natural bridge is temporary and insecure; the falling of blocks from its under side and the general weathering of all its surfaces will weaken it and cause an eventual fall. But new ones appear to be forming to replace those that are lost in the ever changing landscapes of the plateaus.

SAND DUNES
Rocks on the Move

There is a popular misconception that a desert should be covered by shifting sand. The fact is that other materials such as bare rock, gravel, salty earth and hard clay are about as common as sand in most deserts. The word desert comes from the same source as deserted and although sand is sterile and unfriendly to life, it is not the only reason why plants and animals may be absent. Perhaps it is the shifting, moving, ever changing nature of sand that makes it more interesting and dramatic than immobile soil and rock.

Why does sand accumulate in a desert? The wind does not actually blow any harder or more steadily there than at other places, and the underlying rocks which supply the sand are not necessarily more sandy than any other rocks. The real cause of sand accumulation is lack of moisture and vegetation. If sufficient moisture existed, there would be soil and vegetation to hold the soil together and break the force of the wind. As it is, the wind passes over the unprotected earth picking up and moving whatever it can. The finer, lighter particles are soon blown entirely away, out to sea or into distant places where they settle in calmer air. The material that we call sand is coarser and heavier and can be bounced or pushed along but not picked up and carried for long distances. Of course, larger pieces of rock are left behind entirely and not moved at all.

Obviously it takes a long time for the wind to find and bring together the countless grains of sand needed to make a patch of dunes or even a single dune. It is not wind alone or sand alone or even the two together that makes a sandy desert—the real reason is that the wind has nothing to hinder its action for a long period of time.

Why aren't there more sand dunes in the plateau country? The winds are strong enough, vegetation is scanty, and there are plenty of sandy formations. In spite of favorable conditions for the production of dunes they do not have sufficient opportunity to grow and accumulate. The sand of the Plateau lands has only a short journey before it reaches, falls into, and is carried away by one of the several large rivers of the area. If the Colorado River and its tributaries did not traverse the land we would undoubtedly find many extensive areas of sand dunes. Instead of piling up in dunes the sand is carried away by water to the distant Gulf of California.

Here and there where conditions are favorable the traveler in

Sand moves over a hill

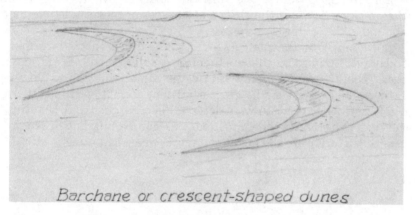

Barchane or crescent-shaped dunes

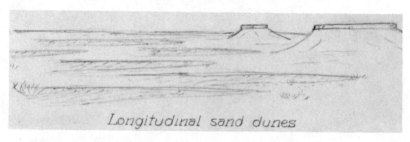

Longitudinal sand dunes

the plateau will nevertheless see a few dunes or perhaps even a large area of drifting sand. Many of these are near cliffs. A dune that has piled against a cliff and has the appearance of trying to climb over it is called a "rising dune"; one that is made of sand that has blown or fallen over a cliff is called a "falling dune". On flat country we may see the picturesque half-moon shaped dunes or barchans with the horns or ends pointing away from the wind. Here also, if there is a little sparse vegetation and not too much sand, we will see the longitudinal dunes, stretched out and streamlined in the direction of wind movement.

When sand is really abundant it forms a solid sheet with sand piled on sand. A few such areas are found in the Southwest and have received special names. Most famous is the White Sands National Monument in Otero County, New Mexico. Here the grains of sand are snowy white gypsum rather than the usual quartz fragments. At the Great Sand Dunes National Monument, in the San Luis Valley of Colorado just west of the Sangre de Cristo Range there are dunes more than 500 feet high.

In Utah just south of the road from St. George to Kanab are the Coral Pink Sand Dunes. The pink sand is distinctive, it comes from the breaking down of the cliffs and surfaces of pink sandstone that abound in the vicinity.

In much of the plateau-country the dunes that are forming today rest upon rocks that are themselves solidified dunes of former ages. These "fossil deserts" show the same structure as do the modern ones. Most of the great sandstone formations in southern Utah are deposits of ancient deserts. The peculiar and beautiful curving patterns in the sandstone are not so puzzling when we realize that they are the inside structures of ancient dunes.

VOLCANOES
How New Rocks Appear

We have discussed many of the ways in which rocks are destroyed, worn down, and carried away to the sea. One might almost assume from a study of erosion that the continents are doomed to disappear and that the oceans in time might cover the earth. But there is another side to the story—for new rocks are made and added to the landscape in the form of volcanic dust, ash, and lava flows. The Southwest is liberally sprinkled with volcanoes of many shapes and sizes that have contributed much material to the landscape. But, not one of these volcanoes is active or alive today. Nevertheless, some are remarkably fresh looking, the contorted lava and frothy cinders around them look almost as if they had cooled only yesterday. The latest known eruptions came about 900 years ago, one of the last ones put the finishing touches on Sunset Crater near Flagstaff, Arizona.

A geologist can recognize and reconstruct on his maps and diagrams the larger and more ancient volcanoes of the Southwest. Not one but many large volcanoes were piled one upon another to build up the Yellowstone Park area in Wyoming and the San Juan Mountains in Colorado. But these great centers passed their prime and became extinct millions of years ago and erosion has obliterated their original forms. The casual traveler is more interested in the younger volcanoes with fresh uneroded cones with cup-like craters in the summits, and with streams of black lava breaking over their rims or through their sides. There are plenty of these, both large and small—over 200 such young cones have been counted in southern Utah and northern Arizona.

There are many kinds of volcanic rock in the West, but the one commonly produced by the latest eruptions is basalt. This rock is hard and dark, almost black; it may be full of bubble-like cavities like bread, or it may be very dense and solid. The term "cinder" is applied to volcanic rock that has been blown out in popcorn-like bits; conical piles of this loose material called cinder cones, are common in the Southwest. Lava may push up to break through the loose cinders and flow like water down the nearest slopes.

A volcanic cone, especially a small one made of loose cinders, is a passing thing that erosion will soon destroy. But each volcano has a root or throat that extends miles downward into the earth, and this

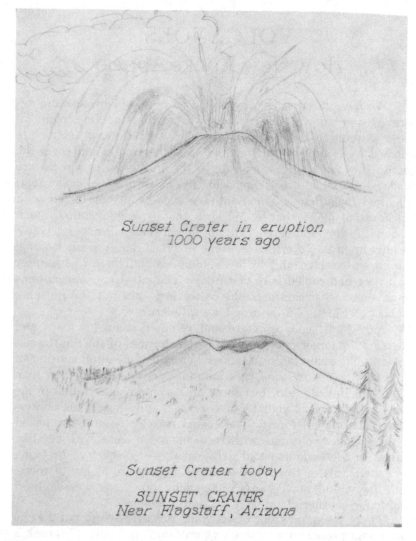

Sunset Crater in eruption
1000 years ago

Sunset Crater today

SUNSET CRATER
Near Flagstaff, Arizona

exists as a prominent feature long after the surface evidences are gone. After a volcano has become inactive the throat is plugged with volcanic rock that never reached the surface or that fell backward in the dying stages of eruption. This solidified material is usually harder than the surrounding rock and, according to the first law of scenery (differential erosion), will stand higher than the surrounding country. Volcanic plugs, or necks as they are called, are mostly circular in outline so that their forms will be that of a spire or pinacle. Near the Four-Corners, especially in the Arizona section, there are dozens of these protruding volcanic necks, dark and mysterious among the red cliffs and mesas of sedimentary rock that surround them. The Navajos and Hopi have given them appropriate names such as The Thumb and The Beast.

Most famous of all volcanic necks of the southwest is Shiprock, a landmark so high and distinctive that it can be seen a hundred miles away. It rises 1800 feet from the plain of soft shale that surrounds it. It is interesting to contemplate how much higher this once stood, how large a surface cone it produced, and how much material has eroded from around it in the ages since it was a surging mass of lava feeding an active volcano.

SHIPROCK, NEW MEXICO
Volcanic neck 1800 feet high

PETRIFIED FORESTS
AND DINOSAUR GRAVEYARDS
Rocks in Disguise

Survival is difficult in the southwestern deserts, and plants and animals are relatively scarce. It has not always been so; there have been times when this now barren area was teeming with plants and animals living on lush lowlands with abundant streams and sufficient food for even the largest creatures.

To tell all that is known about the prehistoric life of the plateau-lands would be out of place here, but our story would be incomplete without mention of the most famous and unusual fossil deposits. Petrified fossils are stones of a special type—stones with shapes determined by the form and structure of things that were once alive. Petrification means "being changed to stone," but fossil forms are not accidental reproductions or "freaks of nature" as was once supposed. Their forms were determined precisely, atom on atom, by preexisting living material such as wood or bone. What is called petrified wood or petrified bone is now truly mineral matter or rock, but the process of petrification or replacement is so nearly perfect in preserving every detail that most people still refer to the stony products as wood or bone.

The areas where the best examples of large fossil deposits are found have been set aside for preservation in special scenic areas—for wood there is Petrified Forest National Park in northeastern Arizona and for bone, the Dinosaur National Monument in northeastern Utah.

Petrified Forest National Park covers a choice outcrop of the Chinle Formation which has fossil wood almost every place it is seen. Forests of cone-bearing trees once grew over much of the Southwest, and many of their trunks were buried under favorable conditions and so became fossils. If we read the story correctly, most of the trees grew along streams or in highlands some distance from the places of their final burial. They were toppled by storms or undermined by rivers after which they were carried away to be stranded on distant mud flats or sand bars. Only a few of the fossil logs have the limbs attached, and even the roots are mostly battered to mere stubs. This indicates strong stream action and perhaps a long journey in a large river.

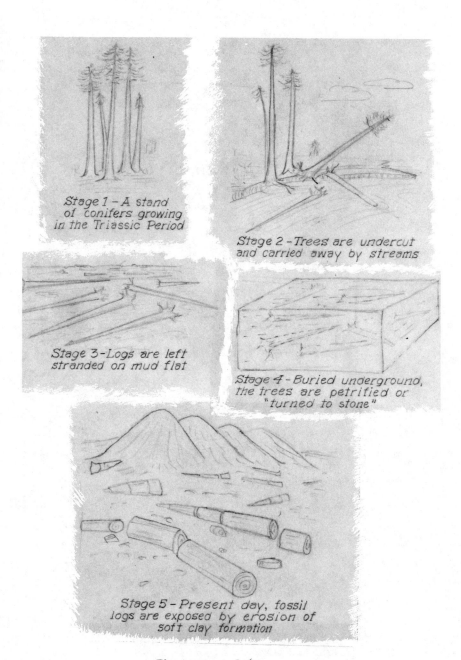

Stage 1 – A stand
of conifers growing
in the Triassic Period

Stage 2 – Trees are undercut
and carried away by streams

Stage 3 – Logs are left
stranded on mud flat

Stage 4 – Buried underground,
the trees are petrified or
"turned to stone"

Stage 5 – Present day, fossil
logs are exposed by erosion of
soft clay formation

The history of the
PETRIFIED FOREST

Dinosaurs drowning at river crossings

Bodies stranded on sand bar

Petrified bones in the Quarry

A Short History of the
preservation of dinosaur bones

Once buried the trees were petrified rather quickly as such things go; this we know because their trunks are perfectly round and uncrushed. Most fossil trees are mashed flat by the weight of overlying sediments. The mud in which the trees of the Petrified Forest National Park were buried was rich in silica, a mineral which is capable of entering and petrifying hard substances very easily at ordinary temperatures. In the silica there were small amounts of iron and other elements which were trapped to give the brilliant colors of the final fossilized wood. Preservation in many logs is very detailed—the yearly rings are clearly visible and even individual cells are plainly seen under a microscope.

Uncounted numbers of fossil logs lie buried in the Chinle Formation tens, hundreds, or thousands of feet underground. Additional numbers have reached the surface and disappeared as chips and dust with the general wastage of the Plateau. The ones we see now are in the process of being uncovered, some nearly perfect, others neatly broken into sections, and many more in chunks and chips littering the landscape. The story of the petrified forest is a lesson in the vastness of time.

More fascinating perhaps is the story of the dinosaurs—a story we can barely touch on here. The dinosaurs roamed western North America for 200,000,000 years, from the time of their beginning to their extinction as a race. The three great periods of dinosaur history are each represented by geologic formations in the Plateau, and there are probably more kinds and sizes of fossilized dinosaurs present here than anywhere else on earth.

So prolific are the petrified bones of the dinosaurs in certain formations that any sharp-eyed "rock hound" can pick up hundreds of pieces in a few hours search. Of course we do not find complete dinosaur skeletons on the surface of the earth: weathering and erosion shatter the individual bones even before they appear to view. Complete skeletons must be dug out carefully from rocks into which weathering and roots have not penetrated. The greatest graveyard of dinosaurs known is that at Dinosaur National Monument near Jensen, Utah. Discovered early in the century, it has yielded parts of over 300 dinosaurs, many of which were complete enough to find a place in the large museums. This site is known to represent an old river bank or sand bar where dead dinosaurs were swept by flood waters and stranded in the shallow water. They may have been drowned one at a time at some upstream point which they tried to cross when the river was in flood stage. Again, like the trees of the fossil forests, the bones were buried and petrified in water-soaked material. Later as erosion reached the right level, the deposit was discovered and opened up to reveal the bones of giant reptiles dead millions of years before.

Other dinosaur graveyards are known but have not been developed for viewing like that of the Dinosaur National Monument. One near Cleveland, Utah has yielded thousands of bones from a soft clay deposit. It seems to have been a bog which captured unwary dinosaurs as they walked over a swampy lowland.

Fossil shells, leaves, footprints, bones, and wood are widespread in the Plateaus. Ask for the local "rock shop," and you will find specimens for sale and perhaps even learn the locality of the local fossil beds.

METEOR CRATER
A Rock from Outer Space

Twenty miles west of Winslow, Arizona is one of the most unusual features of North America. It is now officially called Meteor Crater, but older names such as Coon Butte and Crater Mound are also still in use. It is really a hill with a deep hole on top. The hole is 3500 feet across and its walls are rugged and broken. The central floor, lying 330-350 feet below the rim is soil covered and flat. Outside the rim, on the flanks of the hill are many huge boulders and patches of white sand.

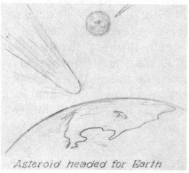

Asteroid headed for Earth

There seems to be little doubt that this is the scar left by the impact of a visitor from space —a meteorite of large dimension. Thousands of pieces of iron-rich meteoritic material have been picked up in the vicinity of the crater, including pieces weighing many pounds up to ten miles away. Evidently the body, which was at least several hundred feet in diameter, was shattered by the impact and most of it rebounded back out of the crater onto the surrounding countryside.

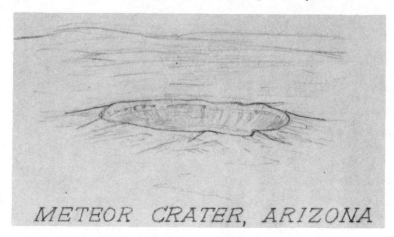

METEOR CRATER, ARIZONA

Before the nature of meteor craters was understood, it was generally believed that a huge and probably very valuable body of iron or nickle-iron lay under the crater floor. No less than 28 deep borings and even several mines were dug or drilled in the hope of finding this valuable material. The total cost of this exploration is said to have been more than $1,500,000.00, but there were no financial returns. It was discovered that the upper 220 feet of material in the hole are lake beds—it once contained a body of water. An additional 1000 feet consists of mixed debris from the walls, and below this is solid rock like that of the surrounding formations.

Pieces of the Canon Diablo meteorite, as it is called, can be seen in many museums, and there have been enough for thousands of amateur collections as well. The original mass certainly weighed thousands of tons, but the exact size cannot be known.

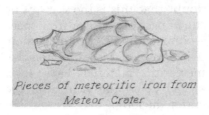

Pieces of meteoritic iron from Meteor Crater

Although it is difficult to tell, it is believed that the meteorite struck northern Arizona about 25,000 years ago. Contrary to all rumors the Indians knew nothing about its origin; it was there long before the ancestors of present-day tribes arrived.

ROCKS FOR MAN
Cliff Dwellers and Pueblos

When man came to the plateau-country, about 10,000 years ago, he was a nomad. He found scanty food, but there were caves in abundance which he could "fix up" to be excellent dwelling places. Whereas his contemporaries in the plains and forests made their homes of sticks, bark, or hides or lived in half-buried "pit houses" covered with earth, the ancient dwellers of the plateaus found ready-made shelters in many canyons and cliffsides. But a cave is not movable or expendable, and dwellers in caves have an incentive to become permanent residents. There are many reasons for staying in one place: to plant and harvest crops, to improve water sources and to cultivate the general surroundings. Thus the people of the plateau became a settled lot; they ceased to follow the herds of game or to wander far and wide to raid or forage. They began to accumulate a few goods, learned to store and pre-serve food, to fashion jars and baskets, and to make themselves comfortable in many ways. Peace was the best way of life under these conditions. Live and let live was a workable creed even though living space became crowded and food at times was scarce.

There were dangers, too, terrible dangers from the less settled, maurading tribes of surrounding areas. The wealth and stored food of the plateau dwellers were a lure and a prize. Soon the settlements which had been free and open were beseiged and had to be fortified. We see hundreds of these fortified places today and call them cliff dwellings or pueblos. Many are not actually in caves but are on hilltops or mesas or huddled against canyon walls. In most of them we sense a feeling of terror; we think of the constant fear of the raiders, of the going to bed only after pulling up the ladders and stopping the passageways. The hand holds, the precarious foot paths, the all-but-inaccessible niches, the hiding places for food, the jars for water—all speak of a fear-ridden existence. Only in a few great centers of population was there an air of safety and security.

What has this to do with the subject of rocks? More than is usually appreciated, for in ancient times the plateau dweller was a user of rocks and adapted to live with a rugged landscape. He was truly in a stone age of existence.

For safety and protection the ancient inhabitants stayed close to the cliffs and canyons. The overhanging ledges, box canyons, and shallow caves, especially those near water, were the sites of their settlements. They utilized rock faces and boulders for walls and cracks for passageways. They built watchtowers on prominent points or mesas, and laid snares and traps for game where the trails narrowed or converged to the water holes. When it became necessary to build walls and dwellings, ancient man became a user of stones on a large scale. Literally millions of individual stones were gathered together to build the larger communities; even the smaller ones represent no small task for unaided human hands. Construction ranged from very crude to very fine—just as today. Some walls were laid up without mortar, others were liberally daubed and strengthened by wet adobe.

Stones for primitive man

It is interesting to look at the hillsides surrounding an old cliff dwelling or pueblo and to see how the area has been picked clean of building stones. Every usable piece for distances of up to a mile has been gathered for construction material. Nature has been kind, however, in providing slabs of rock longer and wider than they are thick for the cliff dwellers' use. A flat rectangular shape is the one most commonly produced from the sandy sedimentary rocks of the desert. Smaller chips serve as chinks between the larger pieces. It is remarkable to see these stone edifices a thousand years old with the thumb prints of their makers preserved on the mortar and plaster.

The typical pueblo or cliff dwelling is not exactly an architectural marvel. There was no moving and fitting of massive stones in

WHITE HOUSE,
CANYON DE CHELLY
Cliff dwellers' refuge

the Inca fashion, and no carving and decorating like that of the Maya or Aztec. The buildings are fragile and precarious, and most are preserved only because they are protected from the weather by overhanging cliffs or their own debris.

Among the hundreds of ancient living centers in the plateau a few stand out and have been designated as National Parks or Monuments. Mesa Verde is the greatest. Here are dozens of large dwelling centers, a number of which have been repaired and made accessible to visitors. Utah shares the Hovenweap National Monument with Colorado. Here, in the open, are well built square towers unlike anything found elsewhere. In northwest New Mexico, about 50 miles southeast of Farmington, is Chaco Canyon National Monument with the pueblo Bonito, a large community dwelling of over 600 rooms. Arizona has Canyon de Chelly, about 60 miles from Kayenta. Here are many dwellings perched in shallow caves beneath tremendous overhanging walls of sandstone.

Not to be overlooked are the stones used for purposes other than building. These were special types prized for grinding food—the well known mano and metate. Other flat stones were used for mixing paints and pigments. Most important of all were those types such as chert, flint, agate, and obsidian used for making tools and weapons. All these have the useful property of being tough and yet brittle. They break along curving fractures which can be controlled to give points or cutting edges. Certain localities were sources of these materials, and the ancient inhabitants traveled miles to collect suitable flint or obsidian for their specific uses.

Not much actual mining was done but the turquoise stone was much valued and traded extensively.